The stories at this level

The plots of the stories at this level are r
should enjoy guessing 'what might con
Encourage this feeling of anticipation a
helps maintain your child's interest. Re
stories equally; it is worthwhile discussing with your children why they
prefer some stories to others.

Your child may be ready to initiate the reading now, by reading through the
story alone on the first read. Don't worry if this doesn't happen. It is still
important that you go on sharing the stories together. Continue the practice
of 'reading together' as before. Suggest that your children join in with the
reading and when they are ready, they give you a signal, like a push on the
arm, so that you stop reading and they continue alone.

Now and again, vary the way you read together by sharing out the
dialogue. Take it in turns for one of you to read the narrative, and the other
to read the characters' speeches. (It would be best on the first read through
for you to take the narrative.) If a word is causing a problem, supply it, so
that the flow of the story is kept going. Mistakes will be made, but this is a
good sign, because it shows that your child is willing to try. Above all don't
stop the reading in mid-stream to correct any mistakes. Wait until the end
of a page or so, and then say "Let's look at that bit again" and read it
yourself, perhaps pointing out the words that were mistaken.

Besides reading the whole story to you, your child will now want to read it
to another audience – a brother or sister, a pet, a doll or a teddy.

Don't rush too quickly onto another book. Remind your child of the stories
that have already been read in the earlier levels. Bring in incidents from the
stories into your ordinary conversation, for example, compare your
breakfast with that of Robbie Robot!

If you have a tape-recorder, you might like to record your reading together.
Let your child read alternate pages with you. Listen to the playback
together; this helps to emphasise the way that the voice makes the reading
more 'interesting'.

The activities at this level

Most of the activities at this level are intended for your child to attempt alone, although help may still be needed with the instructions. Be sure to read through all the activities yourself first – some may involve you as an audience. Emphasise the 'fun' aspect of the activities, and at all costs avoid the impression that they are 'tests'.

There is no need for your child to work through the activities in sequence. If your child glances through to select which activity is the favourite one for today, this will help with the development of the important skills of skimming and scanning (quickly selecting the information you need) when reading material.

Your children might like to build up a 'Book of things I have done from my stories'. This would give a sense of achievement and permanence, as well as enabling you to keep a check on their development and what has been done.

When all the activities have been done, encourage your child to read the story again before you move on to another book.

Robot helps get breakfast

by Helen Arnold

Illustrated by Tony Kenyon

A Piccolo Original
In association with Macmillan Education

Robby Robot was feeling hungry.
"You can help us get breakfast, Robby,"
4 said Anna.

"Get the cornflakes, Robby," said Tony.
"Put some cornflakes in your bowl."

Tony pressed the knob on Robby's head.
"Whirtle-tirtle, whirtle-tirtle. Whirr,"
said Robby Robot.

Robby took out a box.
He shook it into his bowl.

"That's not cornflakes, Robby,"
said Anna.

8   "That's soap powder."

"Whirtle-tirtle. A little muddle,"
said Robby Robot.

"Get the milk, Robby," said Anna.

Tony pressed the knob on Robby's head.
"Whirtle-tirtle, whirtle-tirtle. Whirr,"
said Robby Robot.   11

Robby took out a bottle.
He poured it into his bowl.

"That's not milk, Robby," said Tony.
"That's lemonade."

"Whirtle-tirtle. A little muddle,"
said Robby Robot.

"Get the sugar, Robby," said Anna.

Tony pressed the knob on Robby's head.
"Whirtle-tirtle, whirtle-tirtle. Whirr,"
16　said Robby Robot.

Robby got a box.
He poured it into his bowl.

"That's not sugar, Robby," said Tony.
"That's salt."

"Whirtle-tirtle. A little muddle,"
said Robby Robot.

"Make some toast, Robby," said Tony.

Tony pressed the knob on Robby's head.
"Whirtle-tirtle, whirtle-tirtle. Whirr,"
said Robby Robot.

21

Robby made some toast.

He made more toast.
And he made more toast.

23

"Make him stop, Tony," shouted Anna.
"He's showing off."

24

So Tony turned Robby off.

"Let's eat our breakfast," said Anna.

So Robby ate his breakfast.
But then . . .

"Quirdle-mirdle, huckle-shuckle.
I feel sick," said Robby Robot.
And he was.

27

Things to talk about

1. Robby Robot got everything wrong, didn't he?

What did he get instead of cornflakes?

What did he get instead of milk?

What did he get instead of sugar?

Can you think of some more things that Robby might have got wrong?

2. Do you know what robots are used for?
Why do you think they are useful?

Looking at pictures and words

1. Look at the breakfast table. Draw all the things on the table. Now write the words for the things under the pictures you have drawn.

2. Can you find the words in the story to finish these sentences? Write the sentences out on a piece of paper.

You can ___help___ us get breakfast, Robby.

Put some ___cornflakes___ in your bowl.

Whirtle ___tirtle___. A little muddle.

Robby made some ___toast___.

Tony pressed the ___knob___ on Robby's head.

3. Can you find these words in the word square?

toast   milk   bowl   bottle   salt   sugar

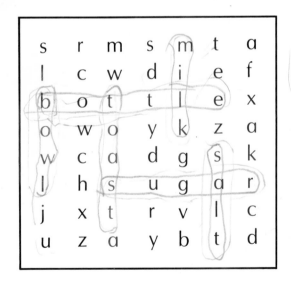

Things to do

What do you think a robot should eat for breakfast?
Draw pictures of what you think Robby should eat and drink.

These activities and skills:	will help your children to:
Looking and remembering	hold a story in their heads, retell it in their own words.
Listening, being able to tell the difference between sounds	remember sounds in words and link spoken words with the words they see in print.
Naming things and using different words to explain or retell events	recognise different words in print, build their vocabulary and guess at the meaning of words.
Matching, seeing patterns, similarities and differences	recognise letters, see patterns within words, use the patterns to read 'new' words and split long words into syllables.
Knowing the grammatical patterns of spoken language	guess the word-order in reading.
Anticipating what is likely to happen next in a story	guess what the next sentence or event is likely to be about.
Colouring, getting control of pencils and pens, copying and spelling	produce their own writing, which will help them to understand the way English is written.
Understanding new experiences by linking them to what they already know	read with understanding and think about what they have read.
Understanding their own feelings and those of others	enjoy and respond to stories and identify with the characters.

First published 1989 by Pan Books Ltd, Cavaye Place, London SW10 9PG

9 8 7 6 5 4 3 2 1

Editorial consultant: Donna Bailey

© Pan Books Ltd and Macmillan Publishers Ltd 1989. Text © Helen Arnold 1989

British Library Cataloguing in Publication Data
Arnold, Helen
Robot helps get breakfast.
1. English language. Readers – For children
I. Title   II. Series
428.6
ISBN 0–330–30225–6

Printed in Hong Kong